In the Name of Allah ﷻ, the Entirely Merciful the Especially Merciful

D1383762

ISLAMIC STUDIES

Activity Book

A Comprehensive International Curriculum

Grade One

Part 1

International Curricula Organization

ALL RIGHTS RESERVED

No part of this book may be reproduced or utilized in any form or by any means, electronic or mechanical, including photocopying, or recording, or by any information storage, or retrieval system, without the written permission of the publisher.

First Edition: 2007 CE. / 1428 A.H.

Islamic Studies, Grade 1 – Activity book, Part 1

© **International Curricula Organization , 2006**

King Fahd National Library Cataloging-in-Publication Data

Team of authors
Islamic studies: Activity book: Grade 1 / Team of authors. – Riyadh
…p; …cm
ISBN: 9960 - 9681 - 6 - 2

1 - English language – Study and teaching – Arabic speakers   1-Title
428,241 dc   1426/5216

L.D. no. 1426/5216
ISBN: 9960-9681-6-2

International Curricula Organization
P.O. Box 225340
Riyadh, 11324
Kingdom of Saudi Arabia
Tel: +966 1 2483688
Fax: +966 1 2483679
Website: www.iconetwork.com
E-mail: info-sa@iconetwork.com

Acknowledgment

While the hard work of all participants in this project deserves recognition, it is however necessary to acknowledge the invaluable contributions of those, who at the helm of affairs, selflessly devoted all their faculties to navigating this project to fruition and for whom this undertaking was indeed a labor of love.

Dr. Abdurrahman Al-Jumhoor (**Late**)
Former General Manager

Dr. Abdulilaah A. Al-Musharraf
Former General Manager

Dr. Qadir Abdus Sabur
Islamic Studies Curriculum Director

Abdullah Al-Badri
Curriculum Science and Methodology

Abdullah Jeena
Islamic Studies Curriculum Coordinator

Members of the Educational Committee

Members of the Technical Committee

Members of the Islamic Studies Committee

Members of the Quality Control Committee

Members of the Editing Committee

Team of Authors

Paul Opoku Addae, United Kingdom

Ashraf Ajam, South Africa

Abdel-Salam Al-Drouby, United Kingdom

Talieb Baker, South Africa

Moegamat Yusuf Feltman, South Africa

Saleem Hassan, United Kingdom

Abdullah Jeena, South Africa

Muhammad Adeel Samodien, South Africa

Introduction

Global educational trends in the past decade were profoundly influenced by learning theories emanating from research in various fields of study such as psychology, sociology, and the neurosciences amongst others. This brought about radical changes in teaching practice, resulting in current trends characterized by a shift in emphasis from conventional teacher-orientated instruction towards student-centered learning focused on student activity.

Sound educational practice accentuates the importance of students actively engaging in valid educational situations in which learning and assessment occur through authentic activities. It is, therefore essential that every learning event incorporate a number of well-structured educational activities. To achieve this, an activity book has been included in this curriculum in addition to the activities and exercises in the Student's Textbook.

This Activity Book is an invaluable resource for both student and teacher, comprising of a collection of supplementary learning and assessment activities to support the content in the Student's Textbook. Although it is presented as a separate entity, the Activity Book is an integral part of the overall educational experience this curriculum offers.

Salient Features

• Activities in this book are organized according to the lessons in the Student's Textbook rather than by topics to make it easy to implement the books in this series as a coherent unit. The activities span all the learning areas as in the Student's Textbook, with the exception of the review lessons. These are not covered in the Activity Book to avoid tedious repetition and employ the available resources to cover as many new topics as possible.

• The curriculum recognizes the differences that exist among individual students and acknowledges the unique learning style of each, which has to be correctly identified, nurtured, and developed. It therefore emphasizes the crucial role that resourceful activities play in facilitating such divergent learning styles. The activities are structured to suit the learning preferences of most learners based on contemporary research.

• This book includes both individual and group activities. Group activities are a vital part of the collaborative learning strategy which facilitates peer support and assessment.

• Activities are particularly designed to be challenging, stimulating, foster creativity, develop critical thinking and to introduce an element of excitement and fun into the learning situation.

• The teacher has an extensive choice of activities to use with students of varied abilities. A particular set of activities may be incorporated into the lesson while another may be used as further enrichment. The aim is not to let students complete all the activities in the book, but rather for the teacher to select appropriate tasks based on the unique characteristics of each class.

• Students are exposed to authentic learning situations akin to real-life settings as opposed to conventional teaching strategies based on a body of text taught out of context.

• The books contain many attractive pictures and illustrations, which enhance the exciting learning experience they aspire to generate.

• Although the activities are of varied complexity, they are all grade-appropriate as far as using suitable language and the skills required to complete them successfully are concerned.

The possible solutions and answers to activities are provided in the Teacher's Manual, which is divided into:

1. A student's section, containing teaching tips and solutions to the activities from the Student's Textbook,

2. An activity section containing information about the activities as well as solutions for the content related to the Activity Book.

Abdulrahman M. Alakeel
General Manager

CONTENTS

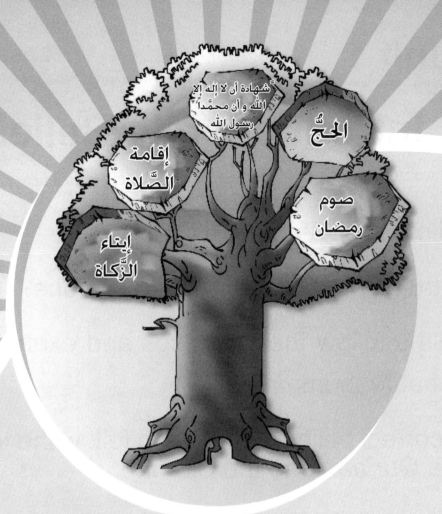

Unit 1

- **Introduction to Belief**
- **The Pillars of Islam**
- **Introduction to the *Qur'aan***

Introduction to Belief

- ⊙ Muslims believe in the truth.

- ⊙ The truth is to believe in Allah ﷻ alone.

- ⊙ Muslims follow the teachings and example of the Prophet Muhammad ﷺ.

- ⊙ The correct belief in Islam is to follow the teachings of the *Qur'aan* and the *Sunnah*.

- ⊙ Muslims also follow the example of the Companions.

Activity

Use (✔) for right and (**X**) for wrong

1- Muslims believe in one god.

2- The *Sunnah* is the teachings of the Prophet ﷺ.

3- Muslims should not follow the example of the Companions.

4- The Qur'aan is the Word of Allah ﷻ.

Activity

Which examples do Muslims follow?
Color the correct circle.

3

Mention a few countries or places where Muslims live.

NOTES

The Pillars of Islam

◉Islam is built on FIVE pillars.

◉Muslims believe in ALL five pillars

◉The FIVE PILLARS are:

1.The *Shahaadah* (the testimony of faith): testifying that there is no god worthy of worship but Allah and that Muhammad ﷺ is the messenger of Allah.

2. *Salah* (prayer)

3. *Zakah* (charity)

4. *Sawm* (fasting the month of Ramadaan)

5. *Hajj*

Activity ①

 Write the Arabic name for each of the five pillars in the spaces below

| Shahaadah | Salah | Zakah | Sawm | Hajj |

Each picture shows the meaning of one of the words. **Write** the number of the picture next to the correct word. (The first has been completed as an example.)

Hajj   **2**

Sawm

Shahaadah

Zakah

Salah

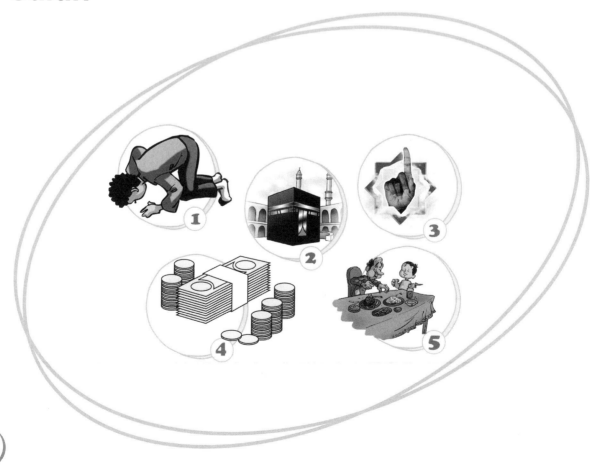

With your classmate, practice saying the *Shahaadah*: "There is no god worthy of worship but Allah ﷻ and Muhammad ﷺ is the messenger of Allah."

There is no God worthy of worship but Allah ﷻ and Muhammad ﷺ is the Messenger of Allah

Activity 4

 With your classmate, practice saying the *Shahaadah* in Arabic.

Complete the list of times in your daily life when you say the *Shahaadah*.

1. Salah

2.

3.

Introduction to the *Qur'aan*

⊙ Muslims believe that the *Qur'aan* is the last Divine Book.

⊙ Allah ﷻ will never send any Divine Book after it.

⊙ Muslims follow the laws in the *Qur'aan*.

⊙ The *Qur'aan* was sent by Allah ﷻ to the Prophet ﷺ.

⊙ The *Qur'aan* has never been changed.

⊙ The *Qur'aan* will never be changed.

Activity ①

 Color in the path that will take you to *Jannah*.

Jahannam   Hajj   **Jannah**

Sawm

Zakah

Shahadah

Salah

Activity

Which laws should Muslims follow?
Color the correct shapes.

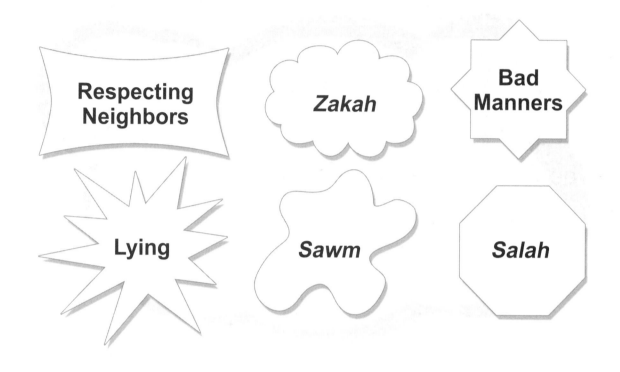

Respecting Neighbors

Zakah

Bad Manners

Lying

Sawm

Salah

Activity

 **Rewrite** the following sentence in its proper order.

love **the Qur'aan**

 I

Which of these two scripts is Arabic and which is English?

The Holy *Qur'aan*

The Holy *Qur'aan*

The Holy *Qur'aan*

القرآن الكريم

أَلْقُرْآنُ الْكَرِيمُ

القران الكريم

Can you read them?
With the help of your family, write "the Holy *Qur'aan*" in Arabic and English.

What is the connection between these pictures and the *Qur'aan*?

أشهدُ أنْ لا إله إلّا اللّه وأنَّ محمّدًا رسولُ اللّه

Unit 2

- The *Shahaadah:* (Part 1)

- The *Shahaadah:* (Part 2)

- Respecting the *Qur'aan*

Unit 2 Lesson 1

The *Shahaadah*: (Part 1)

⊙ The *Shahaadah* is to say the following:

> **"I testify that there is no god worthy of worship but Allah ﷻ and that Muhammad ﷺ is the messenger of Allah."**

⊙ A person has to say and believe in the *Shahaadah* to be a Muslim.

⊙ The *Shahaadah* is the first pillar of Islam.

Activity ①

 We want to open the lock.
Which parts of the key are missing?
Color in the grooves of the key.

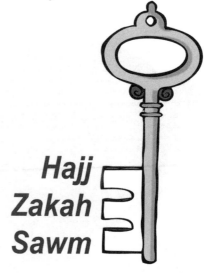

Hajj
Zakah
Sawm

Fill in the missing words to complete the sentence.

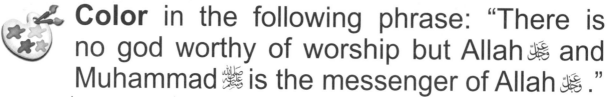

Color in the following phrase: "There is no god worthy of worship but Allah﷿ and Muhammadﷺ is the messenger of Allah﷿."

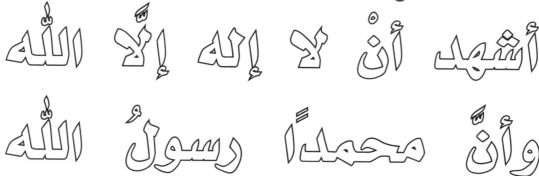

With the help of your family, make some cards of any *dhikr* (prayer) that contain the *Shahaadah*.

Later on, the teacher will decide how you are going to stick your cards around the classroom.

 **Somebody** wants to know about Islam. **Using** the following pictures, guide him or her to the first thing he/she must know.

Unit 2

The *Shahaadah*: (Part 2)

- The *Shahaadah* has two parts.
- The first is: there is no god worthy of worship but Allah ﷻ.
- The second is: Muhammad ﷺ is the messenger of Allah ﷻ.

- Muslims believe that Allah ﷻ sent the Prophet ﷺ.
- Muslims also believe that everything the Prophet ﷺ said is true.

Activity ①

 **Organize** the boxes in the correct order.

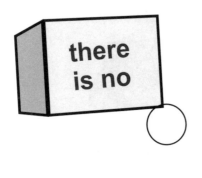 there is no

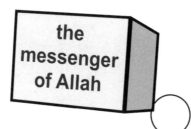 the messenger of Allah

 and that Muhammad is

 but Allah

 god worthy of worship

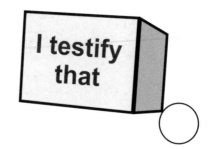 I testify that

18

Name three examples of huge creations of Allah ﷻ. (Students write what they see on the board.)

1- ....

2- ....

3- ....

 Name three examples of small creations of Allah ﷻ. (Students write what they see on the board.)

1- ....

2- ....

3- ....

Color in the word that looks different from the other words in the following sentence.

Allah ﷻ created every thing

An alphabet game:

Each student has to name one of Allah's ﷻ creatures.

The second student names another creature that starts with the last letter of

the one named by the first student.

If a student cannot think of an answer, then he/she is out of the game.

Respecting the *Qur'aan*

⦿ The *Qur'aan* was sent by Allah ﷻ to all people.

⦿ Muslims respect the *Qur'aan*.

⦿ The *Qur'aan* must be handled carefully.

⦿ Do not leave the *Qur'aan* in a dirty place.

Activity ①

Circle all the places in the picture where you would put your *Qur'aan*.

Have a look at the different sizes of the editions of the *Qur'aan* in your home, mosque, or library. **Discuss** this with your classmates.

NOTES

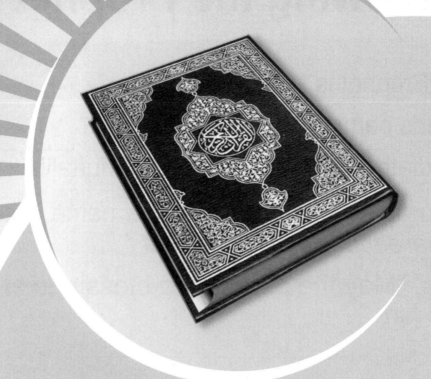

Unit 3

- Knowing the Prophet ﷺ

- Allah ﷻ - The Creator

- Completeness of the *Qur'aan*

Unit 3

Knowing the Prophet

⦿ The last Prophet is Muhammad ﷺ.

⦿ His father's name was 'Abdullaah.

⦿ His grandfather's name was 'Abdul-Muttalib.

⦿ When Muslims hear the Prophet's ﷺ name, they should say: *"sallallaahu 'alayhi wa sallam."*

⦿ It means, "May the peace and blessings of Allah ﷻ be upon him."

Activity ①

Color in blocks number 4, 7 and 8.

1. 'Abdullaah	6. Madeenah	11. Ka'bah
2. Muslims	7. Allah	12. 'Abdul-Muttalib
3. the Qur'aan	8. Messenger	13. Companions
4. Muhammad	9. 'Umar	14. *Hajj*
5. Makkah	10. *Hijrah*	15. *Sunnah*

Color in the following word:

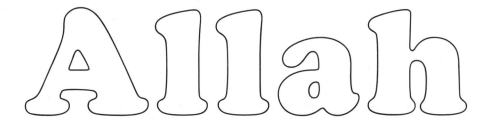

Look at the words in the circle:

Now write a sentence using some of these words:

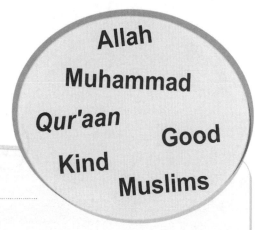

Allah
Muhammad
Qur'aan
Good
Kind
Muslims

Color in the following statement:

Muhammad ﷺ is

The Prophet

of Allah

With your classmates, discuss why we say, *"sallallaahu 'alayhi wa sallam"* whenever we hear the Prophet's name.

NOTES

Allah ﷻ – The Creator

⊙ No one has the ability to create anything from nothing except Allah ﷻ.

⊙ A Muslim believes that Allah ﷻ created everything.

⊙ All of Allah's ﷻ creation shows His Glory.

⊙ Allah ﷻ says, "Your God creates and chooses everything." (*Soorah al-Qasas*: 68)

Activity ①

 Complete the picture and color it.
What is this?

Put the following things where they belong.

Bird	Fish
Cat	Cloud

Unit 3

Completeness of the *Qur'aan*

◉ The *Qur'aan* is a book that Allah ﷻ sent to all people.

◉ It is the final revelation.

◉ The *Qur'aan* is not like any other book.

◉ It has never been changed.

◉ Allah ﷻ has preserved it.

Activity **1**

Your teacher will read to you the story of 'Amr Ibn Salmah.

He led his people in *Salah* while he was still a child and knew more *soorahs* than many other people.

Activity **2**

Your teacher will read to you the story of the man who was bitten by a snake.

When the *Qur'aan* was read for him, he was healed by its power that was given by Allah ﷻ.

Activity **3**

Complete the sentences using the words given below.

(1) my book   (2) my god   (3) my prophet

Allah ﷻ is _____

Muhammad ﷺ is _____

The *Qur'aan* is _____

Activity **4**

Add two good acts that you will do this week.

I will say, *"sallaallahu 'alayhi wa sallam"* whenever I hear the Prophet's ﷺ name.

I will always show great respect for the *Qur'aan* and encourage others to do the same.

_____

_____

_____

Unit 4

- Allah's عَزَّوَجَلَّ Creation

- The Three Principles

- Revelation of the *Qur'aan*

Allah's ﷻ Creation

⊙ Allah ﷻ has created all things around us, whether they are living or non-living.

⊙ Allah ﷻ has created things on the ground and in the air.

⊙ Allah ﷻ has created everything that you can see.

Activity ①

 Can you see five things that Allah ﷻ created ?
Write them down:

Activity ②

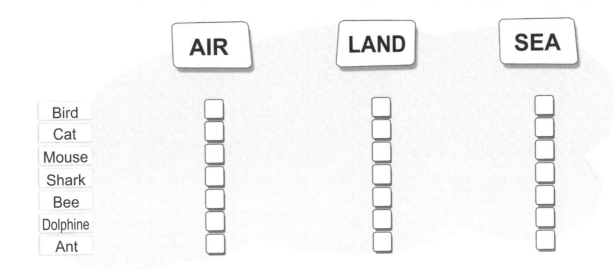

? **Look at** the animals below.
Do they live in the air, on the land, or in the sea?

AIR	LAND	SEA

Bird
Cat
Mouse
Shark
Bee
Dolphine
Ant

Who created all these animals?

Activity ③

What do you see around you?
Draw what you see:

Which are living things and which are non-living things?

Draw

Activity

Find suitable pictures of plants/flowers and paste them in the blocks provided.

Activity

Find suitable pictures of animals and paste them in the blocks provided.

The Three Principles

⊙ Muslims believe in three things:

⊙ The first is that Allah ﷻ is the only *Rabb*.

⊙ The second is that the true religion is Islam.

⊙ The third is that Muhammad ﷺ is the last Prophet.

⊙ Muslims love Allah ﷻ, Islam, and Muhammad ﷺ.

⊙ Muslims love them more than they love themselves and their own families.

Activity ①

Complete the following:
I love Allah ﷻ , because ......

1- ....

2- ....

3- ....

List three reasons why you love Allah ﷻ .

Your teacher will tell you the story about a man whom the Prophet ﷺ asked to reperform prayer three times.

This was because he did not perform it well.

In the end, the Prophet ﷺ taught him how to pray properly.

How does this story teach us the way of offering *Salah*?

 In your class, hold a discussion about the Prophet's ﷺ life and how useful it is for Muslims today.

NOTES

Revelation of the *Qur'aan*

⊙ The *Qur'aan* is a guidance for all people. It was revealed to the Prophet ﷺ through the Angel Jibreel عليه السلام.

⊙ The pagan Arabs could not bring anything like the *Qur'aan*, even though they tried hard.

⊙ The *Qur'aan* helps Muslims in this life and on the Day of Judgment.

⊙ It teaches people the message of the prophets; which is to worship Allah عزّ وجلّ alone.

Activity ❶

 The *Qur'aan* is a guidance for all people.
Find the right path to the *Qur'aan*!
Use the words to find your way.

Activity (2)

To know the process of how the *Qur'aan* came to people, rearrange the following words in the correct order:

○ Jibreel

○ Allah

○ Muhammad

○ People

Activity (3)

Put ✔ or ✖ :

1- **We** received the *Qur'aan* directly from Allahﷻ. ◯

2- **The** *Qur'aan* was revealed in Arabic ◯

3- **Jibreel**﷿ is one of the angels ◯

4- **Allah** ﷻ protects the *Qur'aan* from being changed. ◯

Activity

Look at the map.
With your teacher's help, point out Makkah,
Madeenah, and the holy sites on the map.

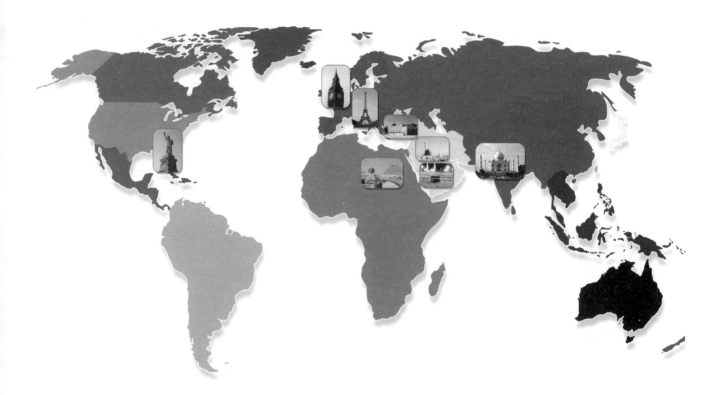

Unit 5

- Allah's ﷻ Creation: Review

- The *Shahaadah*: Review

- The *Qur'aan*: Review

Unit 5   Lesson 1

Allah's ﷻ Creation: Review

- Allah ﷻ created everything.

- Allah ﷻ created all living and non-living things.

- All the things on the ground and in the air were created by Allah ﷻ.

Activity   1

 Allah ﷻ created the rain.
Can you name four things that need **water** to live?

1 _____

2 _____

3 _____

4 _____

Allah ﷻ created **everything**.

DRAW something you **like** and something you **don't like**.

Can you say **why** you do or don't like them?

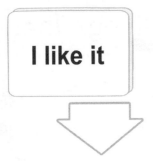

I like it

↓

I don't like it

↓

MAKE A CHART.

Do this at home.

Find pictures of ten things that Allah ﷻ created and paste them onto a chart.

Five of them must be living and five non-living.

Do you know the name of each thing?

Write the names next to the things that you pasted onto your chart.

YOU WILL NEED:

A large sheet of paper or chart / board

Glue

Sticky tape

NOTES

The *Shahaadah*: Review

⊙ Islam is built on five pillars. The first is the *Shahaadah:* "To testify that there is no god worthy of worship but Allah ﷻ and that Muhammad ﷺ is the messenger of Allah ﷻ."

⊙ Muslims worship Allah ﷻ alone, and nothing else. Muslims believe that the Prophet ﷺ is the final messenger of Allah ﷻ.

⊙ Everything the Prophet ﷺ said is true.

Activity ①

 **Color** in the pillars of Islam .

Unscramble the blocks to make this word:

Where was the Prophet ﷺ born?
Mark the place with a blue dot.

Where are you on this map?
Mark the place with a red dot.

48

The *Qur'aan*: Review

- The *Qur'aan* is the final revelation.

- It was revealed by Allah ﷻ through Jibreel ﷺ to Muhammad ﷺ .

- Muslims respect the *Qur'aan*.

- The *Qur'aan* has never been changed.

- The *Qur'aan* helps Muslims to lead good lives .

- We should take good care of the *Qur'aan*.

Activity 1

What does the *Qur'aan* teach us?
Draw lines to show your answers.
The first one has been done for you.

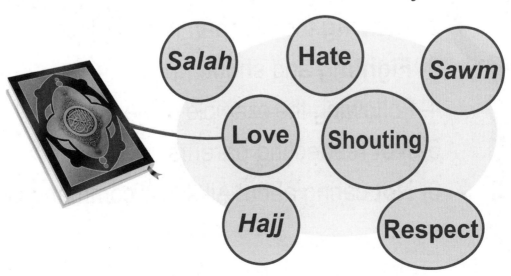

Salah Hate Sawm Love Shouting Hajj Respect

Color in the circles

Allah ﷻ → The Qur'aan → The Prophet ﷺ → Muslims

◉ **This** sign is a warning!
   Place it next to the things you want stopped.

1- **For** Muslims to read the *Qur'aan* ⬜

2- **Leaving** the *Qur'aan* in any place ⬜

3- **Fighting** and shouting ⬜

4- **Following** the example of the Prophet ﷺ ⬜

5- **Not** respecting parents ⬜

6- **Not** caring about Allah's ﷻ commands. ⬜

Unit 6

Unit 6

Introduction to History

⊙ History is very important to Muslims.

⊙ People must know their history.

⊙ It teaches them many lessons.

⊙ It tells them about the Prophet's ﷺ life.

⊙ Muslims must know who the Prophet ﷺ was and how he lived.

⊙ They should follow his example.

Activity ①

Look at the pictures of the Ka'bah throughout history and say which one is old and which is new.

Old ☐ New ☐

Old ☐ New ☐

Color in the Muslim countries.

Can you name five of these countries?

1 ....

2 ....

3 ....

4 ....

5 ....

 1- Write down your Full name.

2- Write down the Prophet's lineage/family tree.

3- Why do you love the Prophet ﷺ. Discuss it with your friend.

A B C D **Complete** the following sentence.

1- **The** Prophet ﷺ was sent to ....

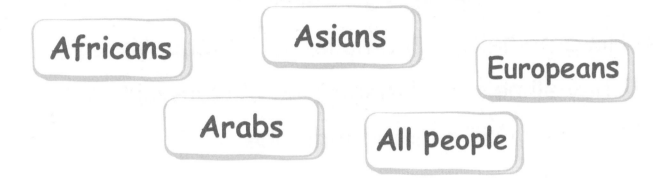

Africans

Asians

Europeans

Arabs

All people

2- **The** Prophet ﷺ was born in

Al-Quds

Madeenah

Makkah

The Name of Prophet ﷺ and His Lineage

⊙ The Prophet's ﷺ name is Muhammad.

⊙ His father's name is 'Abdullaah.

⊙ His grandfather's name is 'Abdul-Muttalib.

⊙ They all belonged to the tribe of Quraysh.

⊙ Quraysh was an important tribe.

Activity

1

 Which of the following men were uncles of the Prophet ﷺ ?

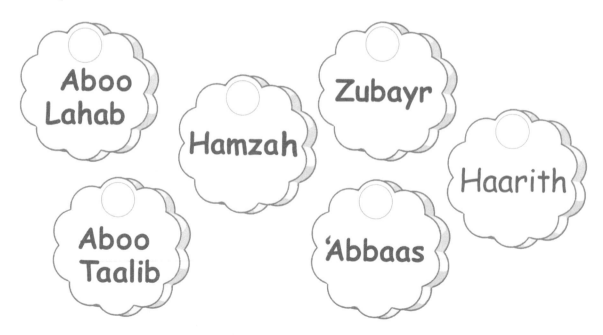

Activity 2

Fill in the blanks.

1. The Prophet's ﷺ name is ....

2. His father's name is ....

3. His grandfather's name is ....

4. They all belonged to the .... tribe.

Activity 3

 Color in the year that the Prophet ﷺ was born in.

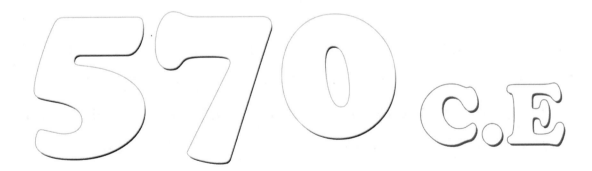

570 c.E

Listen to the story of the Prophet's ﷺ birth. **Your** teacher will tell you a story about the Prophet's ﷺ childhood; being an orphan, how all the wet nurses refused to breast-feed him; and the blessing he brought for his wet nurse, Haleemah As-Sa'diyyah, her donkey, sheep, milk and rain in her village; and Allah's ﷻ protection of him.

Write the name of the Prophet's ﷺ wet nurse.

....

....

....

....

Activity

5

Your teacher will discuss a story with you. (The wet nurses refused to take him because he was an orphan. **Haleemah** As-S'adiyyah agreed to breast-feed him. **She** took him because she did not wish to return to her village without a child).

Unit 6

Reading the *Qur'aan*

⊙ Before Muslims start to read the *Qur'aan*, they have to be clean.

⊙ Muslims make *wudoo'* before they read the *Qur'aan*.

⊙ Reading the *Qur'aan* is the best form of *dhikr*.

⊙ The Prophet ﷺ was always in *wudoo'* when he recited *dhikr*.

⊙ Muslims read the *Qur'aan* in clean places.

Activity ①

To find the word, color in the following columns: 1,3,5,7,9,11,15,17,19,and 21.

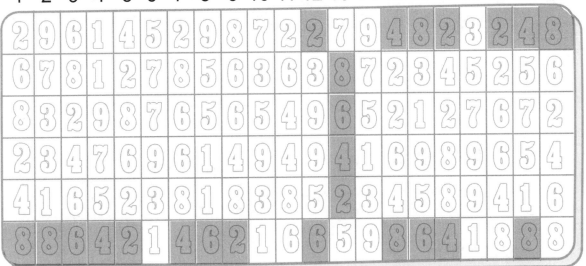

Color in the rooms where you cannot read the *Qur'aan*.

 Put a circle around things you need *wudoo'* for.

SALAH

SLEEPING

DU'AA

TAWAAF

SAWM

WRITING

TALKING

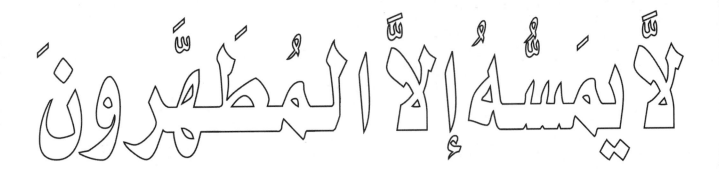

Activity 4

Color in the following *aayah*:

لاَ يَمَسُّهُ إِلاَّ الْمُطَهَّرُونَ

Activity 5

 How could you link the following pictures to the *Qur'aan*?

Unit 7

- **The Prophet's ﷺ Birth and Childhood**

- ***Salah* : The Second Pillar of Islam**

- **Seeking Refuge in Allah ﷻ**

The Prophet's ﷺ Birth and Childhood

- The Prophet ﷺ was born in Makkah, in the 'Year of the Elephant.'

- This was the year when Abrahah from Ethiopia went to Makkah to destroy the Ka'bah.

- The Prophet's ﷺ father, 'Abdullaah, died two months before he was born.

- His mother Aaminah died when he was six years old.

- 'Abdul-Muttalib looked after him until he was eight years old.

Activity ①

What animals did Abrahah take with him when he tried to destroy the Ka'bah?

Activity 2

What happened to Abrahah's army which tried to destroy the Ka'bah?
Draw your answer.

Activity 3

What would life be like without parents?
What can Muslims do to help a person that does not have parents?
Fill in your answers in the shapes below.

Good

Sad

Lonely   Happy

Activity 4

In a group, sing the following song:

My religion is Islam
My full respect to my mom
My book is the Qur'aan
It has the perfect plan
My prophet is Muhammad ﷺ

Activity 5

Color in the following words:

Allah ﷻ **sent His Messenger,** Muhammad ﷺ , **to call people to** Islam.

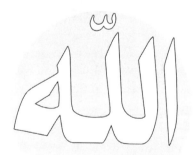

Unit 7

Salah:
The Second Pillar of Islam

⊙ *Salah* (prayer) is one of the pillars of Islam.

⊙ Muslims must pray FIVE times a day.

⊙ The five daily prayers are:

1. *Fajr*   2. *Dhuhr*   3. *'Asr*
4. *Maghrib*   5. *'Ishaa'*

⊙ Muslims are forgiven when they pray and do good.

Activity

1

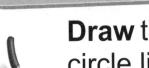

Draw three circles and cut them out. Color each circle like the sun.
Paste the sun onto the spot where it would be in each picture.

Dhuhr   *'Asr*   *Maghrib*

Link the names of the prayers in their correct order.

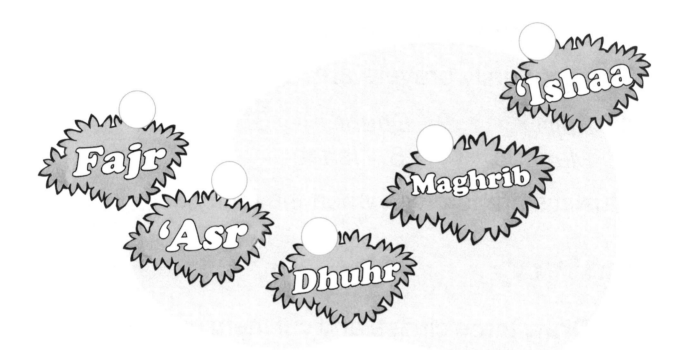

All the students should discuss the following:

You have moved to a new city and there is a *masjid* in front of your house.

How would you introduce yourself to the Muslims living in the area?

How often would you go to the *masjid* and what would you see in it?

Activity

Draw five clocks, and then ask your parents to help you write down the time for each prayer.

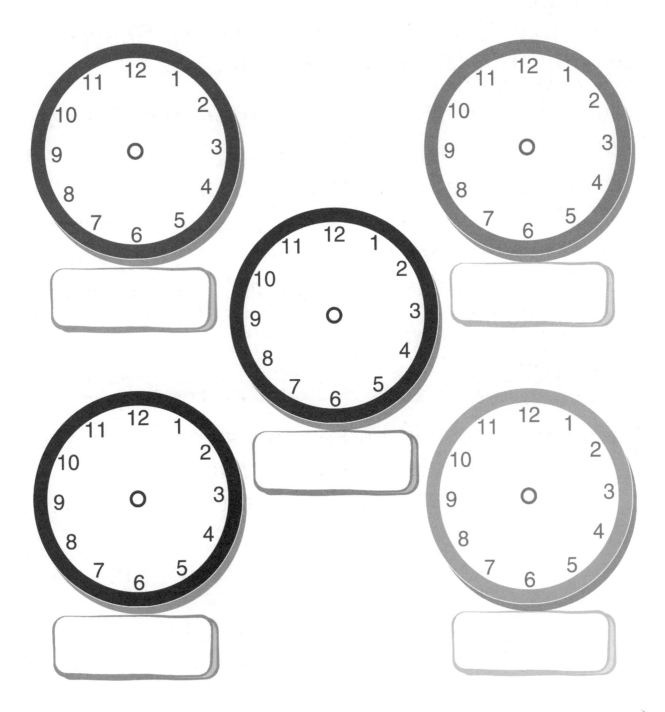

Unit 7

Seeking Refuge in Allah ﷻ

⊙ Muslims seek refuge in Allah ﷻ, before reading the *Qur'aan*.

⊙ They say: "*A'oodhu Billaahi Min ash-Shaytaanir-rajeem.*" This is called *isti'aadhah*.

Allah ﷻ says: "*So when you recite the Qur'aan, (first) seek refuge in Allah ﷻ from Shaytaan, the expelled (from His mercy).*" (Soorah an-Nahl: 98)

⊙ After Muslims seek refuge in Allah ﷻ, they say: "*Bismillahir-Rahmaanir-Raheem.*" This is called the *basmalah*.

Activity **1**

 Someone has broken the signs which show when Muslims say the *basmalah*.
Fit the pieces together to find the answers:

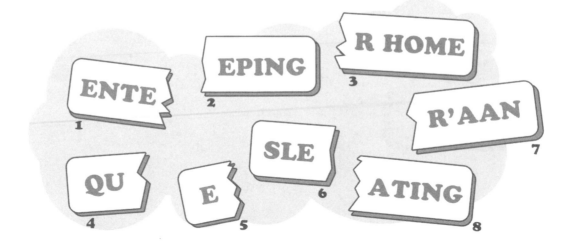

ENTE 1
EPING 2
R HOME 3
QU 4
E 5
SLE 6
R'AAN 7
ATING 8

Activity

 Underline the odd one out in each row.

a'oodhu	after	*isti'aadhah*	*billaahi*

basmalah	worship	lion

Shaytaan	evil	love

Muslims	*Qur'aan*	good	air	recite

heavy	protection	seek	refuge	help

Look at the pyramid made of eggs.

Color in the eggs containing actions for which you say the basmalah.

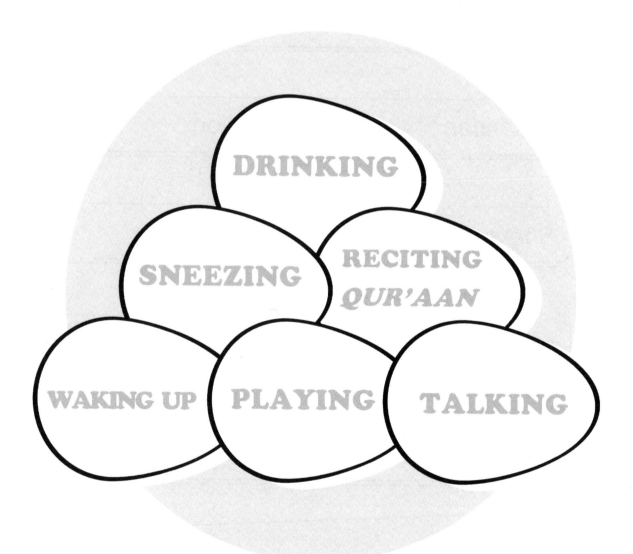

DRINKING

SNEEZING

RECITING QUR'AAN

WAKING UP

PLAYING

TALKING

Activity 4

Say the *isti'aadhah* and the *basmalah*?

Activity 5

On what occasions do you say the *isti'aadhah* or the *basmalah* in your daily life?

Activity 6

Ask your teacher to tell you the story of Aadamﷺ and *Shaytaan*.
Why does *Shaytaan* hate human beings?

Unit 8

- The Five Daily Prayers

- How to Perform *Salah*

- *Soorah al-Humazah :*
  The Slanderer (Part 1)

The Five Daily Prayers

⊙ **Muslims pray FIVE times a day.**

Fajr	the prayer before sunrise	2 Raka'aat
Dhuhr	the prayer after midday	4 Raka'aat
'Asr	the prayer in the late afternoon	4 Raka'aat
Maghrib	the prayer just after sunset	3 Raka'aat
'Ishaa'	the prayer late in the evening	4 Raka'aat

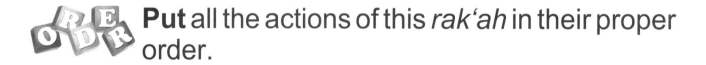

Activity ①

ORDER **Put** all the actions of this *rak'ah* in their proper order.

Activity ②

Draw three clocks like the one below on your page.
On each clock, draw the hands to show the time in your city for:

| Fajr | Dhuhr | Maghrib | 'Asr |

Activity ③

Below are different shapes.

Each shape shows one *rak'ah* of a prayer.

Color the similar shapes with the same color and draw the correct shape next to the prayer.

Fajr

Dhuhr

'Asr

Maghrib

'Ishaa'

How to Perform *Salah*

◉ **Before** Muslims pray they must:

- Have *wudoo'*.

- Cover their body.

- Face the *qiblah* (in the direction of Makkah).

- Pray on time.

- Make the correct intention.

Activity 1

 **Put** the following actions of *Salah* in the correct order.
Number them from **1** to **8**.

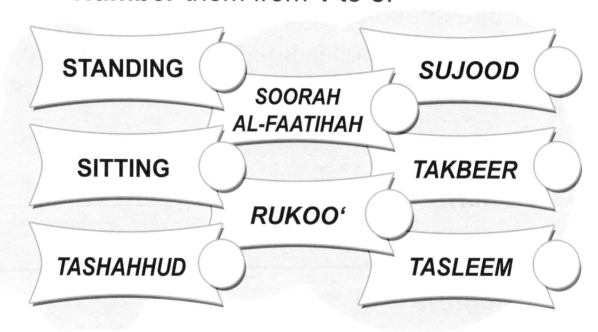

STANDING ◯   SOORAH AL-FAATIHAH ◯   *SUJOOD* ◯

SITTING ◯   *TAKBEER* ◯

RUKOO' ◯

TASHAHHUD ◯   *TASLEEM* ◯

Activity

Cross out the pictures which are not actions of *Salah*.

Where is the Ka'bah?
Mark the place with a red dot.

Look at the seven cities.
Mark their *Qiblah*.
Draw a line from each city to the *Qiblah*.

Soorah al-Humazah:
The Slanderer (Part 1)

⊙ This *soorah* is about backbiting and piling up wealth.

⊙ People pile up wealth thinking they will live forever.

⊙ Allah ﷻ will punish people who do this.

Activity

1

Color in the following *aayah*.

وَيْلٌ لِّكُلِّ هُمَزَةٍ لُّمَزَةٍ

Which one comes first in the *soorah*? Is it A or B?

Soorah al-Humazah

A People backbiting

B Money

Match the pairs.
Color in the blocks using **red** for one pair and **blue** for the other.

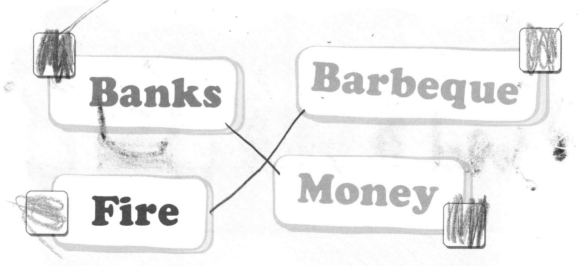

Banks

Barbeque

Fire

Money

Unit 9

- Practical *Salah*

- *Zakah*: The Third Pillar

- *Soorah al-Humazah*:
  The Slanderer (Part 2)

Unit 9

Practical *Salah*

- When Muslims pray together, this is called *jamaa'ah*.
- Allah ﷻ rewards Muslims more if they pray together in the *masjid*.
- Muslim men should love to pray together in the *masjid*.
- It is better for Muslim women to pray at home.

Look at this group of Muslim men and women.

Khadeejah prays
in the *masjid.*

'Eesaa
prays in the *masjid.*

'Abdullaah
prays in the *masjid*.

'Aamir prays at home.

Maryam prays at home.

Which of the men will receive the most reward?

Which of the two women is praying in the most suitable place?

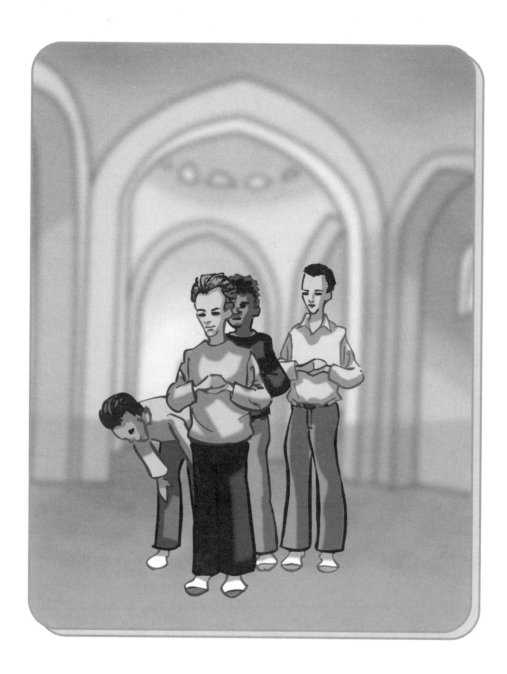

Activity

2

Circle the mistake.

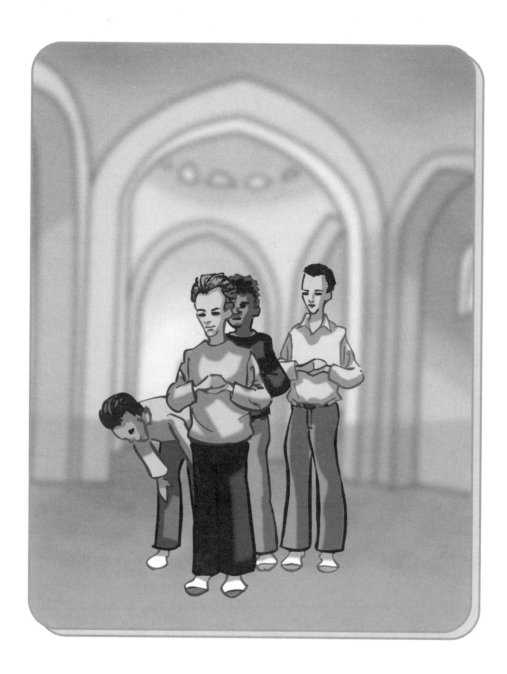

Activity **3**

Link the following pictures with the correct words:
group *masjid* praying alone

group	*masjid*	praying alone

Activity **4**

With your teacher, discuss the differences between praying on your own and praying in *jamaa'ah*.

Unit 9

Zakah: The Third Pillar

⊙ *Zakah* is the third pillar of Islam.

⊙ Muslims who have more than they need must pay *Zakah*.

⊙ *Zakah* is paid to eight types of people.

⊙ Some of these people are the poor and needy.

⊙ It is a Muslim's duty to help those who are in need.

Activity ①

 Sit with a **friend**.
Draw pictures of the ways in which you can **help the poor**.

Color in the following word.

ZAKAH

Activity **3**

Complete the following?

We give Zakah to:

- Help the poor and needy
- Feed the poor

Activity **4**

 In your group, name some of the people who deserve to receive *Zakah*.

Soorah al-Humazah:
The Slanderer(Part 2)

◉ The backbiters will enter *Al-Hutamah*.

◉ *Al-Hutamah* is a very hot fire.

◉ This fire will cover them completely.

◉ The doors of this fire are expanded.

Activity ①

 Color in the correct group of pictures according to the way they appear in the *soorah*. Is it **A** or **B**?

A
Pillars
Fire
Hearts

B
Fire
Hearts
Pillars

Color in the following aayah.

نَارُ اللّٰهِ الْمُوقَدَةُ

Put or after the following statements:

- *Al-Hutamah* is a flaming fire in which only people whom Allah ﷻ does not like will be put. ☐

- Allah ﷻ does not like the rich person who does not give *Zakah* to the needy. ☐

Which of the following deeds can lead you to Hell?

a. Talking about others behind their backs

b. Talking badly about others' honesty

c. Not giving *Zakah*

d. All of them

Unit 10

- **Salah: Review**

- **Prophet Muhammad ﷺ: Review**

- **Review : Soorah al-Humazah**

Salah : Review

⊙ The second pillar of Islam is *Salah*.

⊙ Muslims have to pray five times a day.

⊙ The five daily prayers are:
Fajr, Dhuhr, 'Asr, Maghrib, and *'Ishaa'*

- *Fajr* consists of two *raka'aat.*
- *Dhuhr, 'Asr* and *'Ishaa'* consist of four *raka'aat.*
- *Maghrib* consists of three *raka'aat.*

Activity 1

You have **3** arrows.
Which numbers do you have to hit to equal the total number of obligatory *raka'aat* **of** the five daily prayers?

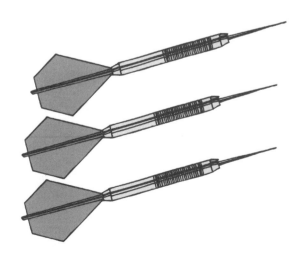

🅰🅱🅲🅳 **Which** of these items will go in the suitcase?

Salah

5

Money

Food

Hajj

Rukoo'

Tasleem

Charity

Poor

Sajdah

Standing

Sawm

Right or wrong?

Use for right and for wrong

- The *tasleem* comes at the end of *Salah*.

- *Fajr* is prayed after sunrise.

- Men should pray the five daily prayers at home.

- *Salah* starts with the *takbeer.*

Unit 10

Prophet Muhammad ﷺ: Review

- Our Prophet's ﷺ name is Muhammad ﷺ.
- His father's name was 'Abdullaah.
- His mother's name was Aaminah.
- The Prophet Muhammad ﷺ was the last messenger of Allah ﷻ.
- Muslims believe that the Prophet Muhammad ﷺ came with the truth.
- All Muslims love the Prophet Muhammad ﷺ.

Activity 1

The Prophet's ﷺ family tree is in the wrong order. Correct it.

Aboo Lahab
'Abdul-Muttalib
Haashim
Hamzah
'Abbaas
Haarith
Muhammad
'Abdullaah
Quraysh
Zubayr
Aboo Taalib

Color in the words connected to the Prophet Muhammad ﷺ.

HERO

BRAVE   GOOD

TRUSTWORTHY

 Draw anything you love.

Unit 10

Review:
Soorah al-Humazah

⊙ **Recitation** and memorization of this *soorah*.

⊙ **What** are the basic ideas of this *soorah* ?

Activity 1

Sit in pairs.

Recite the *soorah* to each other.

Activity 2

Correct your mistakes.

Recite the *soorah* again and try to do it without making any mistakes.

Activity 3

Once you learn one *soorah* perfectly, proceed to the next one.

Revise the meaning of the *soorah* and try to know it perfectly.

Unit 11

- The Benefits of *Zakah*

- *Zakah* is an *'Ibaadah*

- *Soorah al-'Asr* : Time

Unit 11

The Benefits of Zakah

- *Zakah* is a form of worship.
- A person who gives *Zakah* will receive more in return.
- *Zakah* helps those who are in need.
- *Zakah* brings the rich and the poor closer to each other.
- Paying *Zakah* saves a person from Allah's ﷻ punishment.

Activity 1

You should know the word below.
Use the **four** stickers to complete this important word:

Stickers ⬭ ⬭ ⬭ ⬭

Shade the blocks that describe actions which will **not** make Allah ﷻ happy with you!

To love others

To boast

To give money to the needy

To talk about your new things all the time

To give the poor a place to stay

To hate others

To think only of yourself

To tell others about your new clothes

To send food to the poor

To say hurtful things to others

Read the message that was sent on a cell phone. **Write** your message to a needy friend on the other cell phone.

I can help!
Call me if
you need me
to help you.

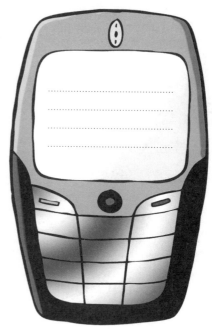

Your teacher will tell you the story of two men. One of them gives *Zakah* to the needy and the other does not. Allah ﷻ blesses the first man, so he succeeds in his business and people love him. The second man loses all his money and becomes poor. When his neighbor sees him among the needy people, he recognizes him. He thanks Allah ﷻ for His blessings, and gives the second man some money.

With your classmates, discuss the following pictures.

Color in the word 'Zakah'.

ZAKAH

Zakah is an 'Ibaadah

⦿ Giving *Zakah* is an *'ibaadah*.

⦿ Allah ﷻ rewards Muslims who give *Zakah*.

⦿ There are two types of *Zakah*:
- *Zakah al-Maal*
- *Zakah al-Fitr*

Activity ①

If you had the chance to help someone else, how would it make you feel?

Write a poem about how you feel when you are good to others.

Mention the word *Zakah* in your rhyme.

Your teacher will divide your class into groups.

In your group discuss ways in which *Zakah* can help the poor people in the world.

Each one in the group should draw a picture about *Zakah* and poverty in the world.

Choose one person from your group to tell the rest of the class what your group discussed.

Activity 3

Collect pictures of the following people:

1. A picture of a rich person.
2. A picture of poor people.
3. A picture of a family.
4. A picture of a crowd.

Show the pictures to your class.

Tell them something about each of the pictures that you have collected.

You may even make up a story about *Zakah* for each picture.

On the picture of the crowd, circle all those whom you think should give *Zakah*.

Soorah al-'Asr: Time

⦿ Allah ﷻ takes an oath by time that man is in loss,

⦿ Except those who believe and do good deeds,

⦿ Those who help each other with the truth,

Those who help each other with patience.

Activity (1)

Match the words below with the clues to complete the *soorah*.

Write the words in the spaces provided below each clue.

A | **Helping an old person**

B | **Al-'Asr**

- Lost
- Good deeds
- Time

C | **Does not know where to go**

Activity

Complete the *soorah*.

Put the following words in the way they appear in the *soorah*. Start from the left.

a) Lost

b) Time

c) Good deeds

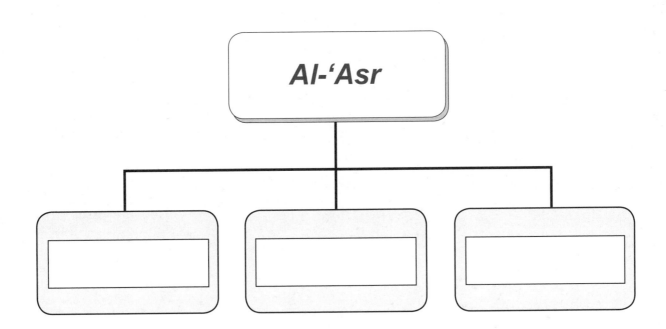

Unit 12

- *Sawm* of Ramadaan: The Fourth Pillar
- The Merits of Fasting in Ramadaan
- *Soorah at-Takaathur*: The Piling-Up (Part 1)

Sawm of Ramadan:
The Fourth Pillar

⊙ *Sawm* is the fourth pillar of Islam.

⊙ Muslims fast by not eating or drinking anything from the beginning of dawn to sunset.

⊙ They fast in the month of Ramadaan.

⊙ *'Eed al-Fitr* is one of the Muslims' celebrations after Ramadaan.

Allah عَزَّوَجَلَّ says:

> *"Believers! Fasting has been made a must for you, like it was made on people before you. So that you become aware of Allah عَزَّوَجَلَّ."* (Soorah al-Baqarah: 183)

Activity ①

You want to break your fast while in a balloon.
You can only take three things with you.
Choose from the things below.

Color in the Islamic celebrations.

MOTHER'S DAY

'EED AL-FITR

CHRISTMAS

BIRTHDAYS

'EED AL-AD-HAA

Color in the Islamic festivals.

Activity 4

With your classmates, discuss how different your family's life becomes in Ramaadan.

Activity 5

In Ramadaan, millions of Muslims, including rich and poor people, stop eating and drinking during the daytime.

They are happy doing that.

Discuss in your groups why someone is happy in Ramadaan, even though *Sawm* might be difficult.

Unit 12

The Benefits of Fasting in Ramadaan

- In Ramadaan the doors of Paradise are opened, and the doors of Hell are closed.

- There is a special door in Paradise called Ar-*Rayyaan*, and only those who have fasted can enter Paradise through it.

- The *du'aa* of a fasting person is accepted.

- *Sawm* is a shield against the fire of Hell.

- Allah ﷻ forgives the sins of those who fast.

- Allah ﷻ rewards the fasting person.

Activity 1

 Which letters go in each letter box ?

Gardens

Sawm

Ar-Rayyaan

Paradise

Hell

Punishment

Ramadaan

Fire

Reward

Color in the sentence that is most important to you.

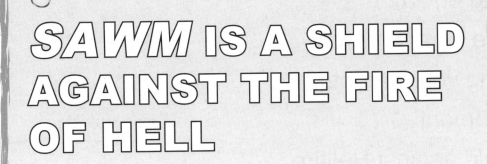

SAWM IS A SHIELD AGAINST THE FIRE OF HELL

ALLAH ﷻ FORGIVES THE SINS OF THOSE WHO FAST

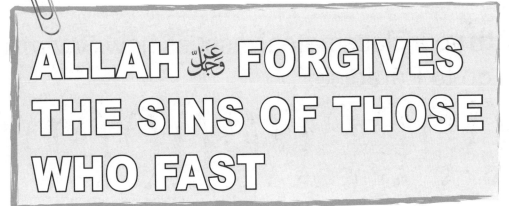

THE DU'AA OF A FASTING PERSON IS ACCEPTED

Good or bad? Place a tick to show your answer.

	Good	Bad
Sawm	☐	☐
Making *du'aa*	☐	☐
Hellfire	☐	☐
Helping your parents	☐	☐
Punishment	☐	☐
A shield against Hellfire	☐	☐

Activity 4

With your classmates, discuss how *Sawm* helps us go to Paradise.

Soorah at-Takaathur:
The Piling-Up (Part 1)

⊙ The gathering of wealth keeps people busy until they die.

⊙ After they die, they will see what happens in the grave.

Activity

What is this picture about?

What does Allah ﷻ say about it in this *soorah*?

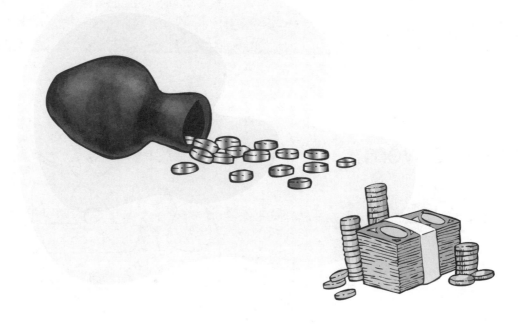

Arrange the following puzzle to complete the *soorah*.

What does Allah ﷻ mention first?

> ## Soorah at-Takaathur

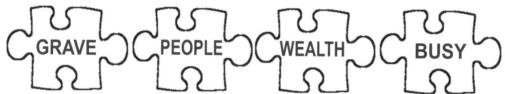

GRAVE   PEOPLE   WEALTH   BUSY

Activity ③

Color in the following word.

Unit 13

- The Manner of *Sawm*

- *Hajj:* The Fifth Pillar

- *Soorah at-Takaathur:* The Piling-Up (Part 2)

The Manner of *Sawm*

⊙ Ramadaan is a special month for Muslims.

⊙ They spend it differently from other months.

⊙ They have an early morning meal called *Suhoor*.

⊙ *Suhoor* is eaten before the *Fajr* prayer.

⊙ After *Suhoor* Muslims do not eat or drink anything.

⊙ Muslims do more good deeds during Ramadaan.

⊙ At *Maghrib* time, they have *Iftaar* (break fast).

⊙ After *'Ishaa'* prayer, Muslims perform the *Taraaweeh* prayer.

Activity (1)

 Put the following words in the correct window of the bus.

Activity

Clean the parts of the board that will spoil your fast.

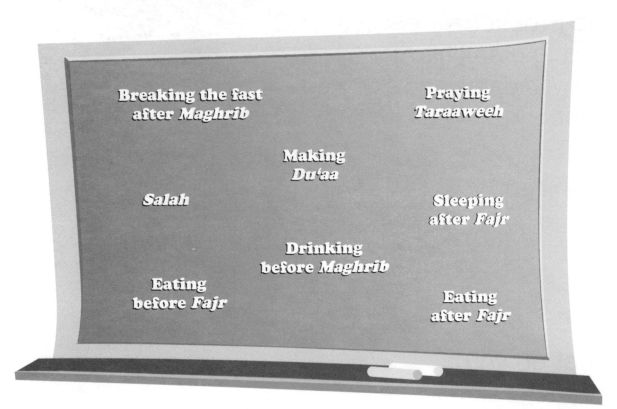

Breaking the fast
after *Maghrib*

Praying
Taraaweeh

Making
Du'aa

Salah

Sleeping
after *Fajr*

Drinking
before *Maghrib*

Eating
before *Fajr*

Eating
after *Fajr*

The Prophet ﷺ used to break his fast with dates and water.

Draw it here.

What do you like to break your fast with?

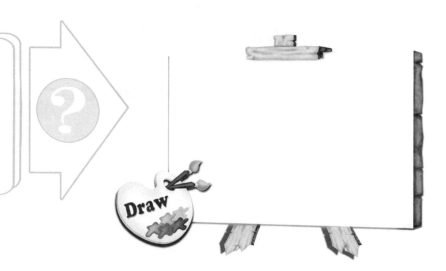

Draw

 With your classmates, discuss the advantages of Ramadaan.

Hajj: The Fifth Pillar

- *Hajj* is the pilgrimage to Makkah in Arabia.
- A Muslim must go for *Hajj* once in his/her lifetime, if he/she is able to do so.
- *Hajj* is the fifth pillar of Islam.
- *Hajj* is very important to all Muslims.
- The Ka'bah is the House of Allah ﷻ.
- The Ka'bah is the first place a pilgrim goes to in Makkah.
- The Ka'bah is also the last place a pilgrim goes to before he leaves Makkah.

Activity ❶

Work in **pairs**.
Build a model of the Ka'bah.
Work with clay!
Build a model of the Ka'bah just like the one in the picture.
Your teacher will show you other pictures of the Ka'bah.

Draw a line to show the route from your city to Makkah.

How will you get there?

Does it cost a lot of money to get there?

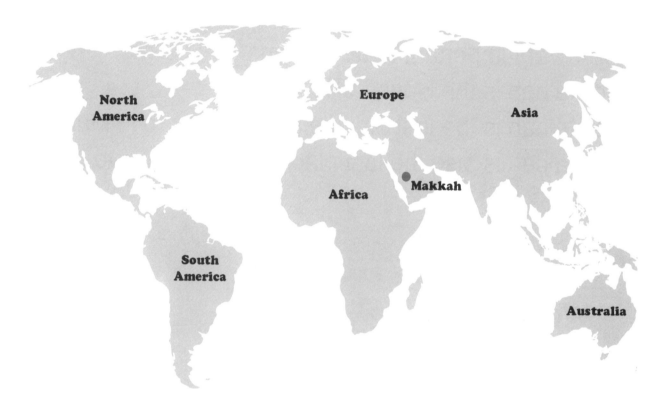

Ask your parents or any family member to tell you about their *Hajj*.

Tell the class about your discussion with this person.

Unit 13

Soorah at-Takaathur:
The Piling up (Part 2)

- Allah ﷻ says that He will definitely show the blazing Fire to those who are piling up their wealth.

- Allah ﷻ will question everyone on the Day of Judgment about the good things He gave them.

Activity ①

Place the following verses in their correct order.

a. Then you will surely be asked that Day about pleasure. ☐

b. Then you will certainly see it with the eye of certainty. ☐

c. You will Surely see the Hellfire. ☐

Activity

Color in the following verse.

ذَلِكَ لِمَنْ خَشِيَ رَبَّهُ

Activity

Go from start to finish passing through the letters on your way.
Collect all the letters to find out the words they make.

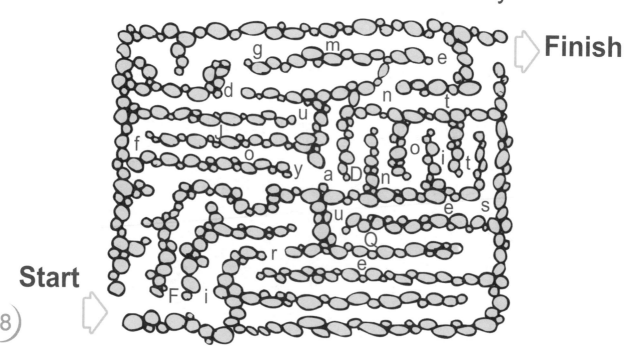

Finish

Start

Unit 14

- ## The Merits of *Hajj*

- ## Practical *Hajj*

- ## *Review:*
  Soorah al - 'Asr,
  Soorah at-Takaathur
  ## (Parts 1 & 2)

The Merits of *Hajj*

- ⊙ *Hajj* is one of the best actions that a Muslim can perform.

- ⊙ There are many benefits for the person who performs *Hajj*.

- ⊙ If a Muslim performs *Hajj*, it will wipe away his sins.

- ⊙ Those who perform *Hajj* are the guests of Allah ﷻ.

- ⊙ The reward for *Hajj* is Paradise.

- ⊙ Muslims learn true unity from performing *Hajj*.

Activity ①

 How will you change your ways after *Hajj*?
Color in the changes you will make.

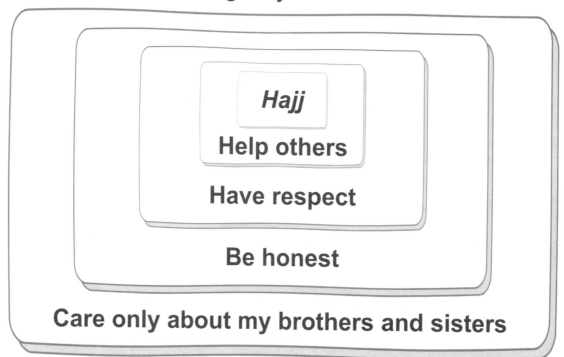

Hajj

Help others

Have respect

Be honest

Care only about my brothers and sisters

Discuss the answer to the following question:
What makes millions of Muslims long to perform *Hajj*?
List the main points that come out of your discussion and read them out to the class.

Activity 3

Color in the following name.

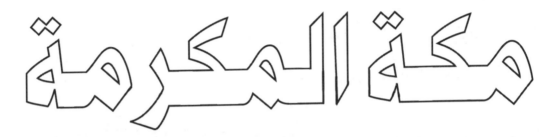

مكة المكرمة

Activity 4

Why would you love to go for Hajj?

Discuss it with your friend in class.

131

Practical *Hajj*

⊙ Muslims perform *Hajj* in the month of Dhul Hijjah.

⊙ *Hajj* consists of a number of actions.

⊙ Each action of *Hajj* must be performed at a certain time.

⊙ All the actions of *Hajj* are done at an exact time.

⊙ The places visited during *Hajj* are:

Al-Masjid Al-Haraam - Mina - 'Arafaat - Muzdalifah

Activity ①

Match the **pictures** with the **places** in the circles:
(Use Arrows)

Look at the picture of pilgrims stoning the *jamaraat* at Mina.

Why do you think Muslims are happy to stone the Jamaraat?

Discuss it with your friend in class.

Activity

3

Put the following pictures in the correct order, so that you can complete the *Hajj* journey.

Activity

4

What do you understand from the following *hadeeth*?

Discuss it in a group and present your answer to your class.

"The virtuous Hajj has no reward except Paradise." (*Ahmad*)